THE BAR MITZVAH BOOK

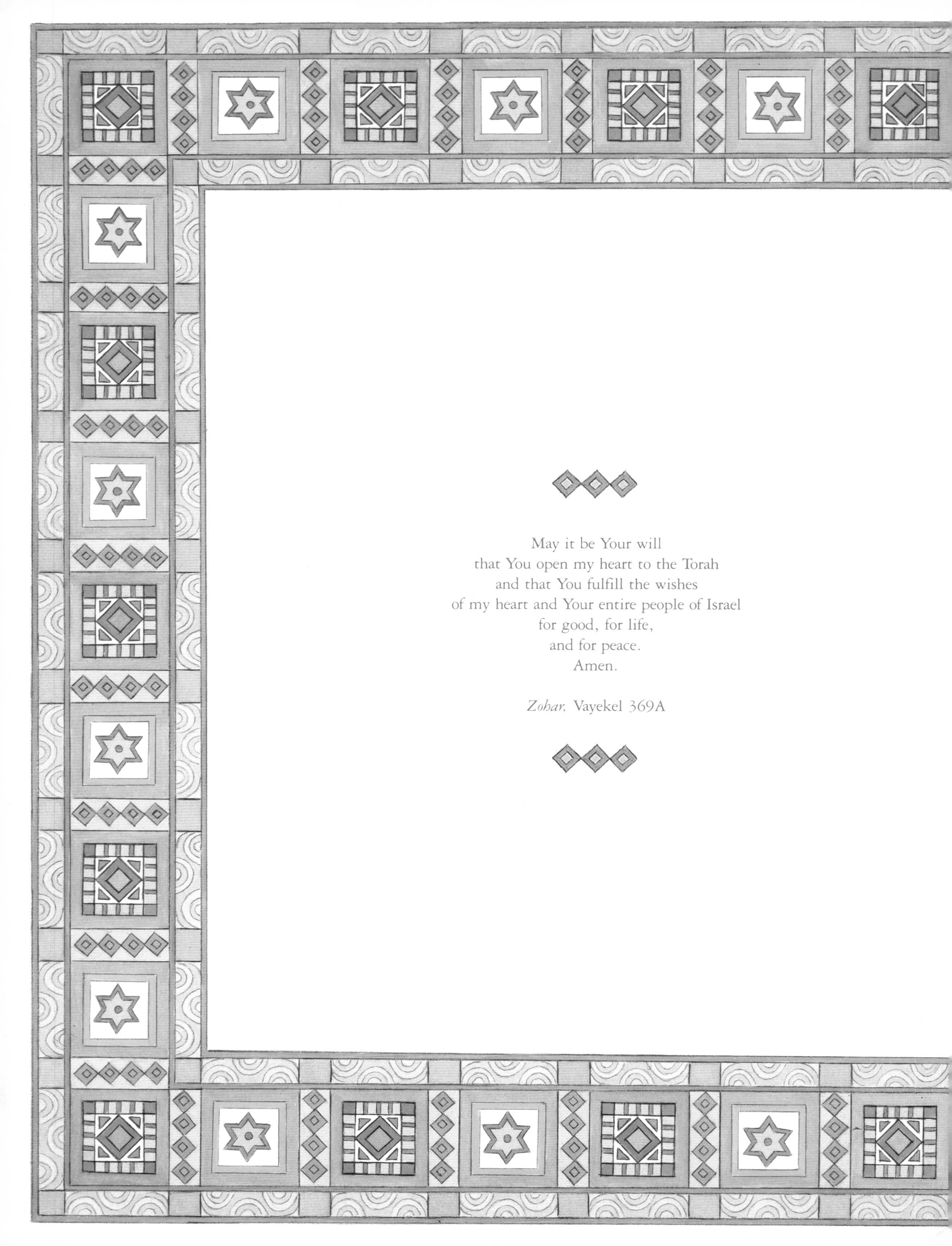

May it be Your will
that You open my heart to the Torah
and that You fulfill the wishes
of my heart and Your entire people of Israel
for good, for life,
and for peace.
Amen.

Zohar, Vayekel 369A

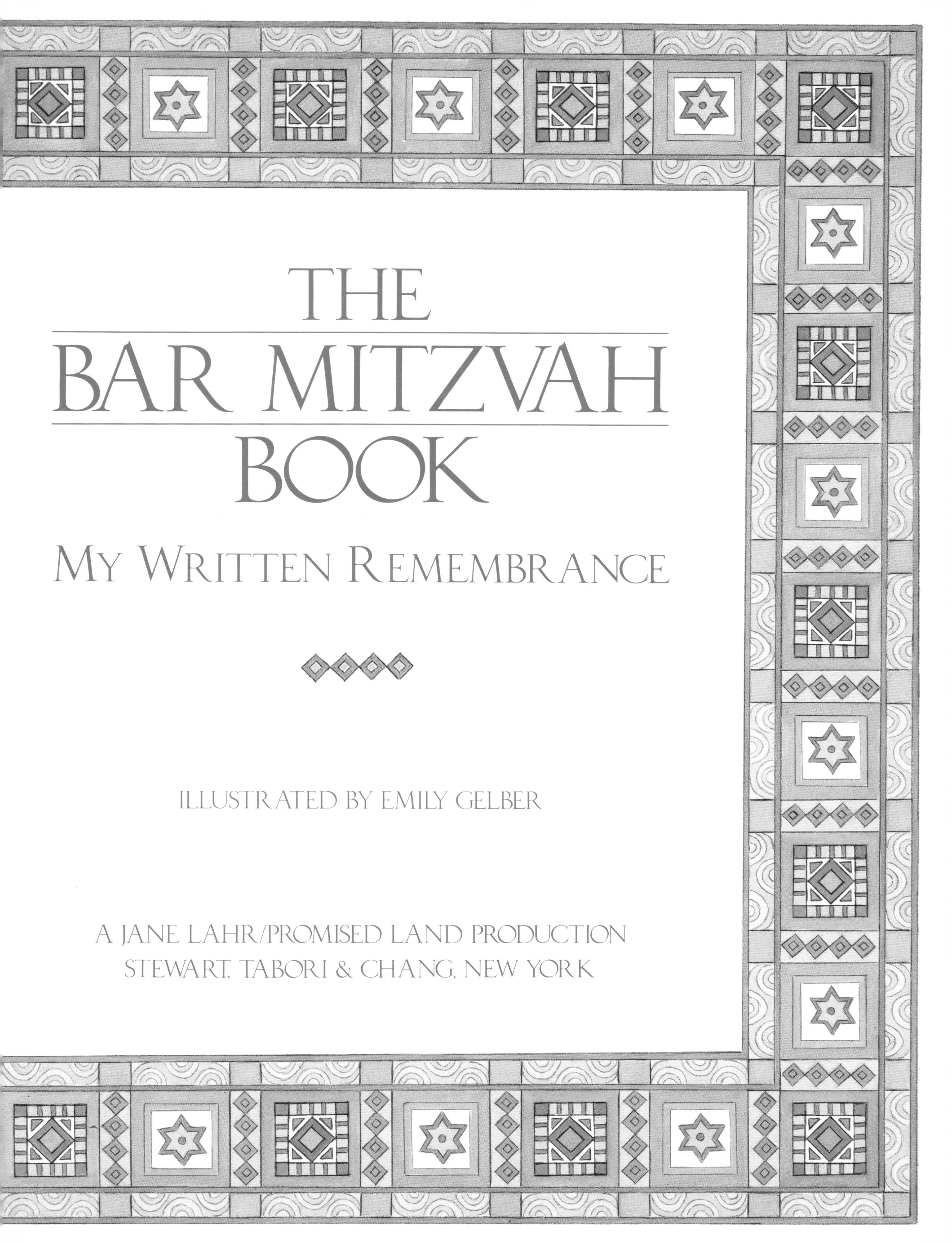

THE BAR MITZVAH BOOK

MY WRITTEN REMEMBRANCE

ILLUSTRATED BY EMILY GELBER

A JANE LAHR/PROMISED LAND PRODUCTION
STEWART, TABORI & CHANG, NEW YORK

Design by Paul Zakris.

88 89 90 91 92 10 9 8 7 6 5 4 3 2 1

ISBN 1-55670-021-0

Published by Stewart, Tabori & Chang, Inc.
740 Broadway
New York, NY 10003

Distributed by Workman Publishing
708 Broadway
New York, NY 10003

Printed in Italy.

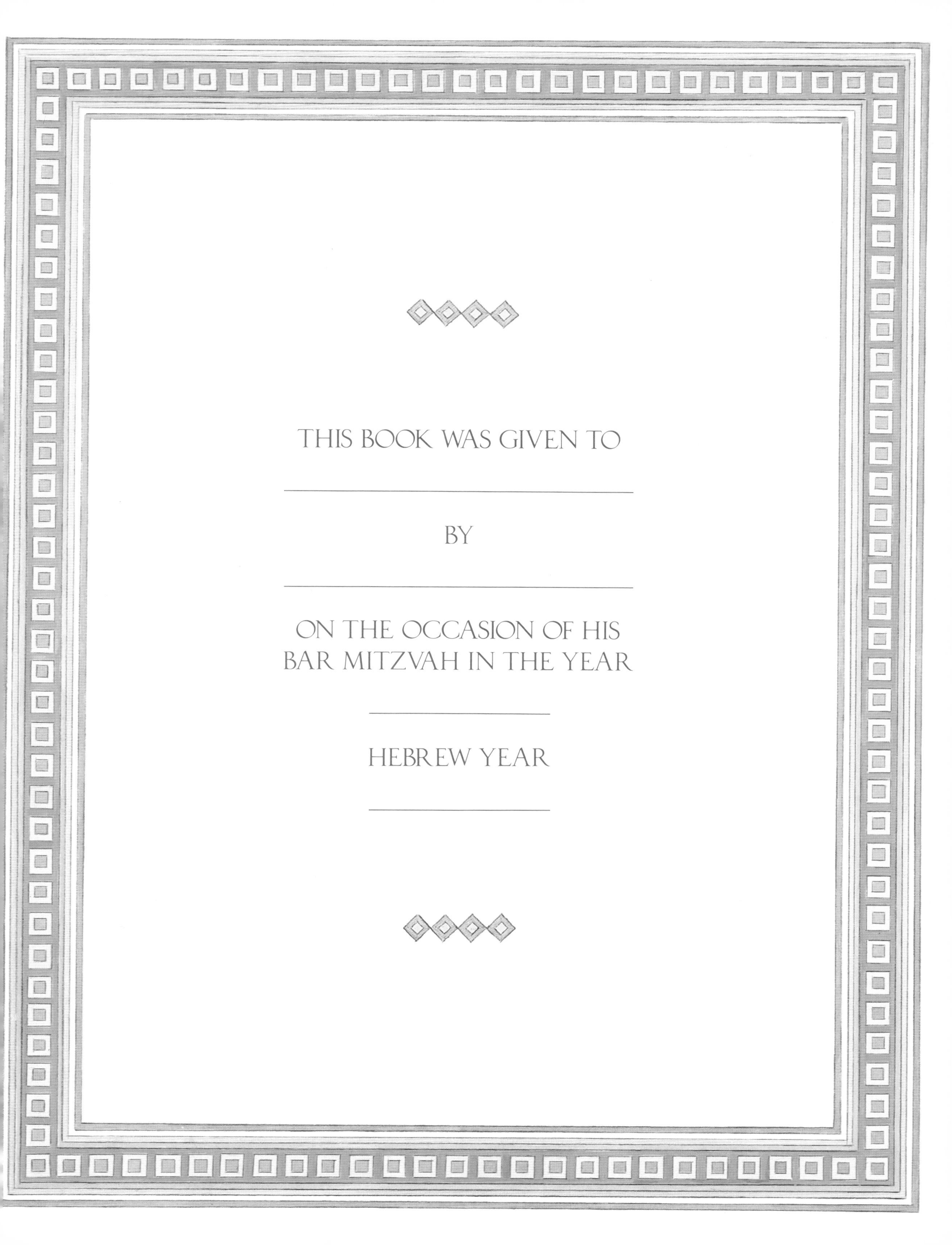
THIS BOOK WAS GIVEN TO
BY
ON THE OCCASION OF HIS
BAR MITZVAH IN THE YEAR
HEBREW YEAR

CONTENTS

MY HISTORY

I was born on ______________________ *in* ______________________

to ______________________ *(née* ______________________ *)*
(mother)

and ____ .
(father)

My Jewish name is ______________________________________ ,

which means ______________________________________ .

I share this name with ______________________________________

____

____ .

I am the ______________________ *child in our family, which also*

includes ______________________________________

____

____

____ .

We live at ______________________________________

____ .

MY SCHOOLING

I go to school at ______________________ *where I am in*

the ______ *grade. My teacher is* ______________________ .

My favorite subject is ______________________ .

My hobbies include ______________________

____

____

______________________ ,

and my favorite sport is ______________________ .

The most exciting thing that has happened to me this year is __________

____

______________________ .

What I look forward to most is ______________________

____

____

______________________ .

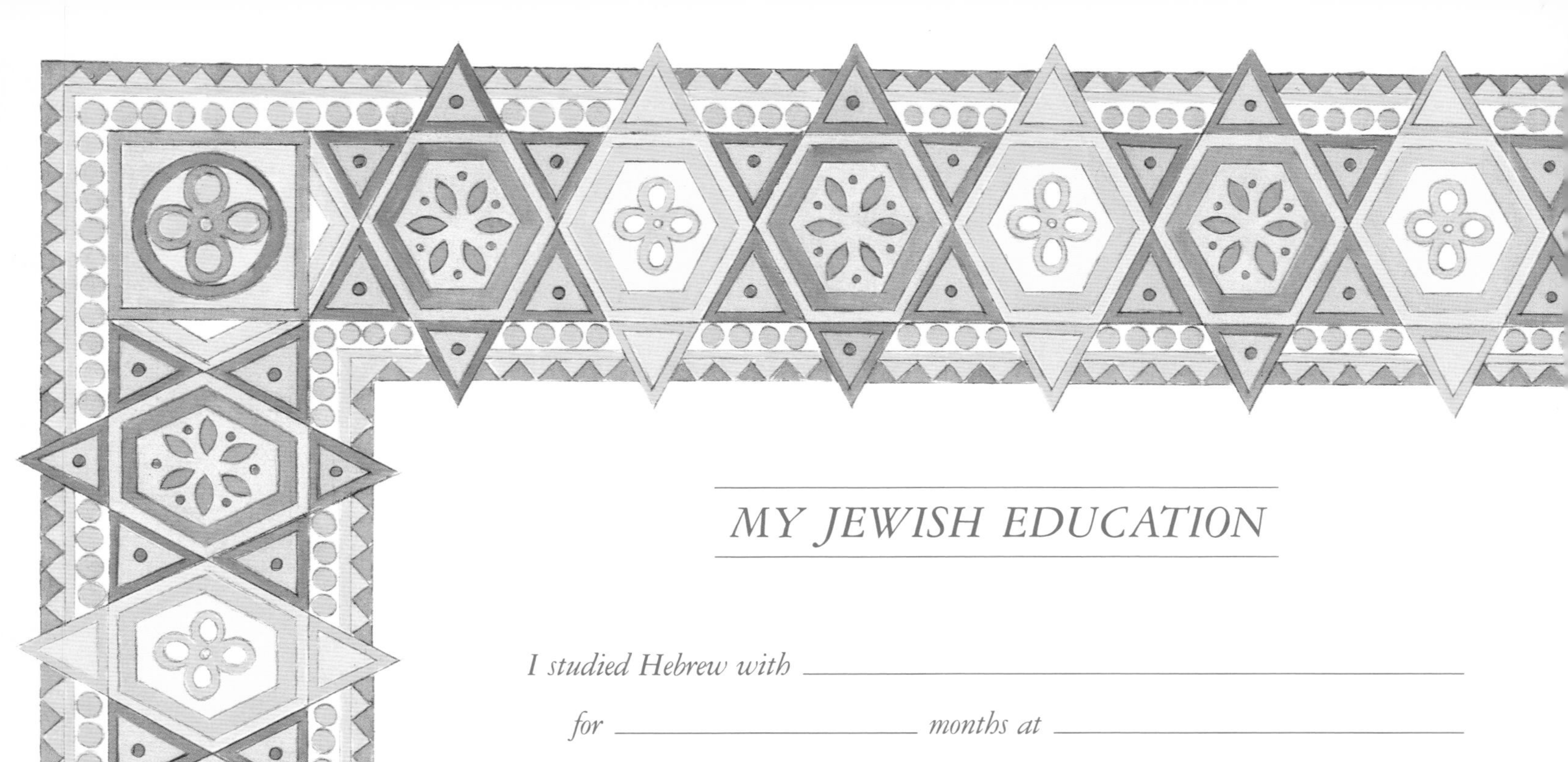

MY JEWISH EDUCATION

I studied Hebrew with ______________________________

for ______________ *months at* ______________________

____ .

We belong to ______________________________ *Synagogue,*

where ______________________________________ ,
(Rabbi)

____ ,
(Cantor)

and ____ *preside.*
(Assistant Rabbi)

I think my greatest accomplishment in the course of my Hebrew education was:

____

____

____

____

____

____

____ .

The most valuable lesson I learned was ____.

The experience was important to me because ____.

MY MOTHER'S HISTORY AND BACKGROUND

My mother's family originally came from a place called ______________________

____ ,

which is in ______________________________________ .

They settled in the United States in ______________________ .

My maternal grandmother was named ______________________ ,

and my grandfather was named ______________________ .

My maternal great grandparents were ______________________

and ______________________ *, and* ______________________

and ______________________________________ .

A favorite anecdote about my mother's family is ______________________

____

____

____

____

____

____ .

MY FATHER'S HISTORY AND BACKGROUND

My father's family originally came from a place called ____________________

____,

which is in ______________________________________.

They settled in the United States in ____________________________.

My paternal grandmother was named __________________________,

and my grandfather was named ____________________________.

My paternal great grandparents were ____________________________

and ______________________, *and* ______________________

and ____.

A favorite anecdote about my father's family is ______________________

____

____

____

____

____

____.

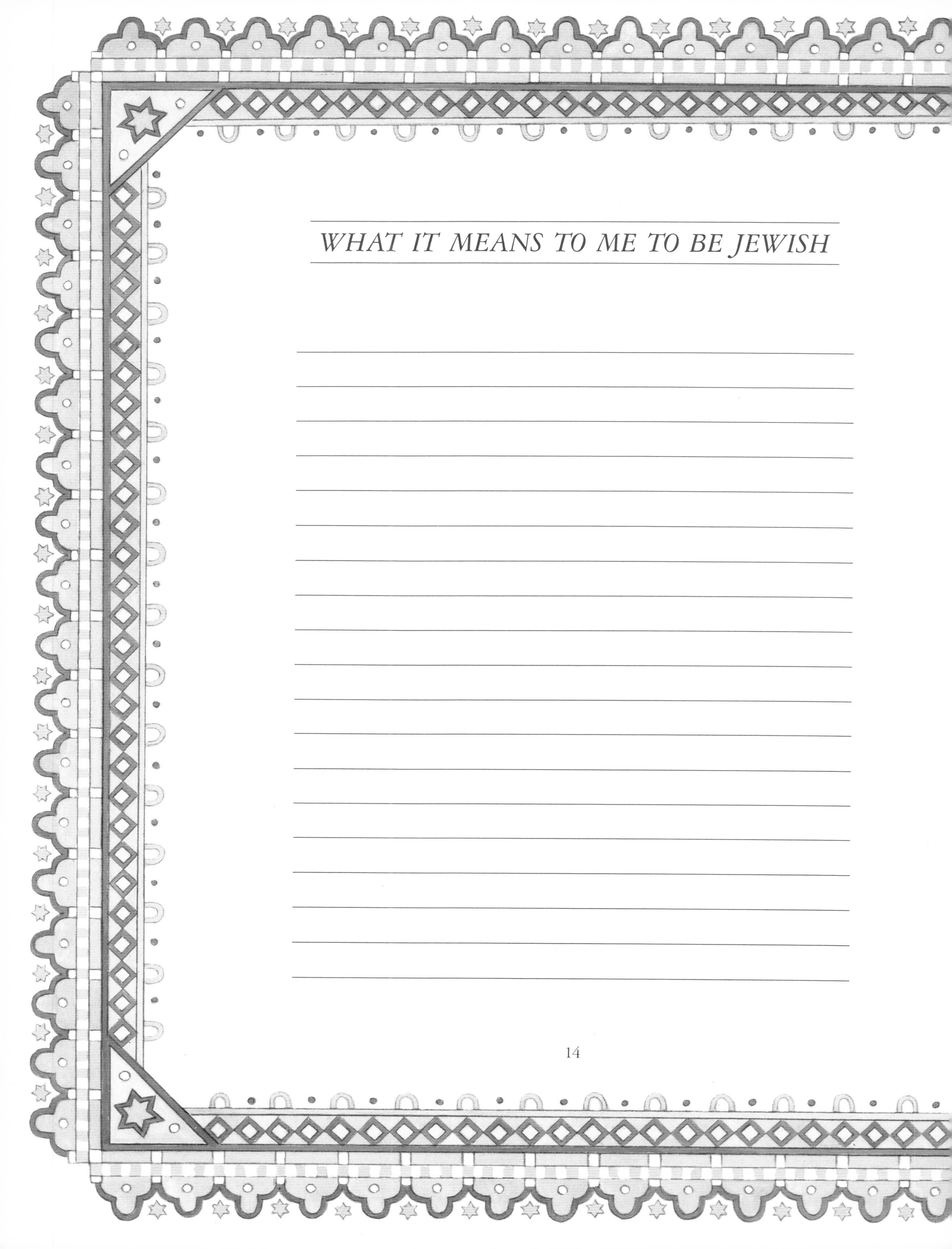

WHAT IT MEANS TO ME TO BE JEWISH

My son, do not despise the Lord's discipline
or be weary of his reproof,
for the Lord reproves him whom he loves,
as a father the son in whom he delights.
Proverbs 3:11–12

PREPARING FOR THE CELEBRATION

The celebration was planned by ______________________________

______________________ *with* ______________________ .

At the celebration we will be serving: ______________________

____

____

____

____

____

____

____

We have invited ______________________ *people to join us.*

Some of the special people we have invited are ______________

____

____

____

____

____

____ .

The friends I have invited to the party are ________________

____

____

____

____

____

____

____ .

OUR INVITATION

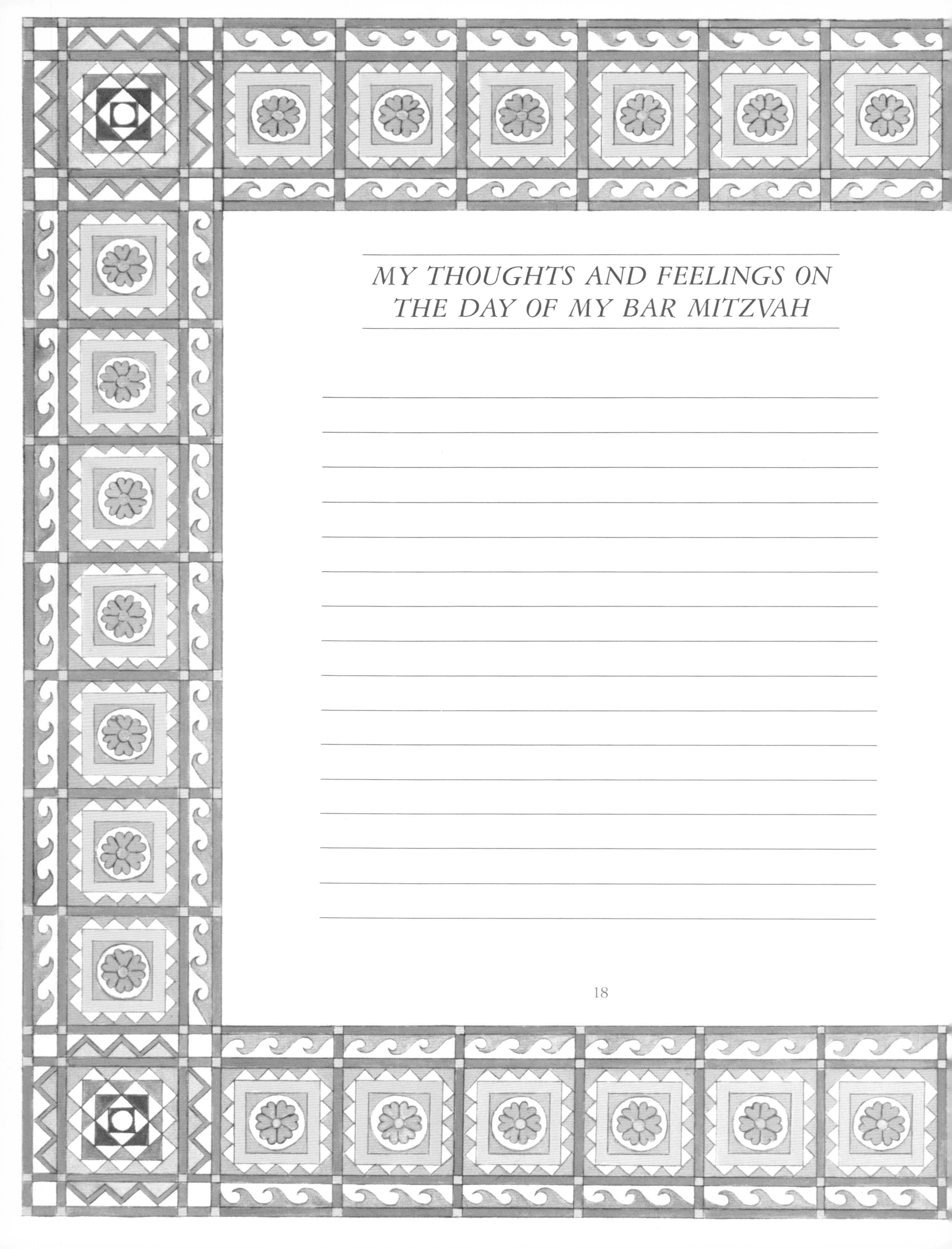

MY THOUGHTS AND FEELINGS ON THE DAY OF MY BAR MITZVAH

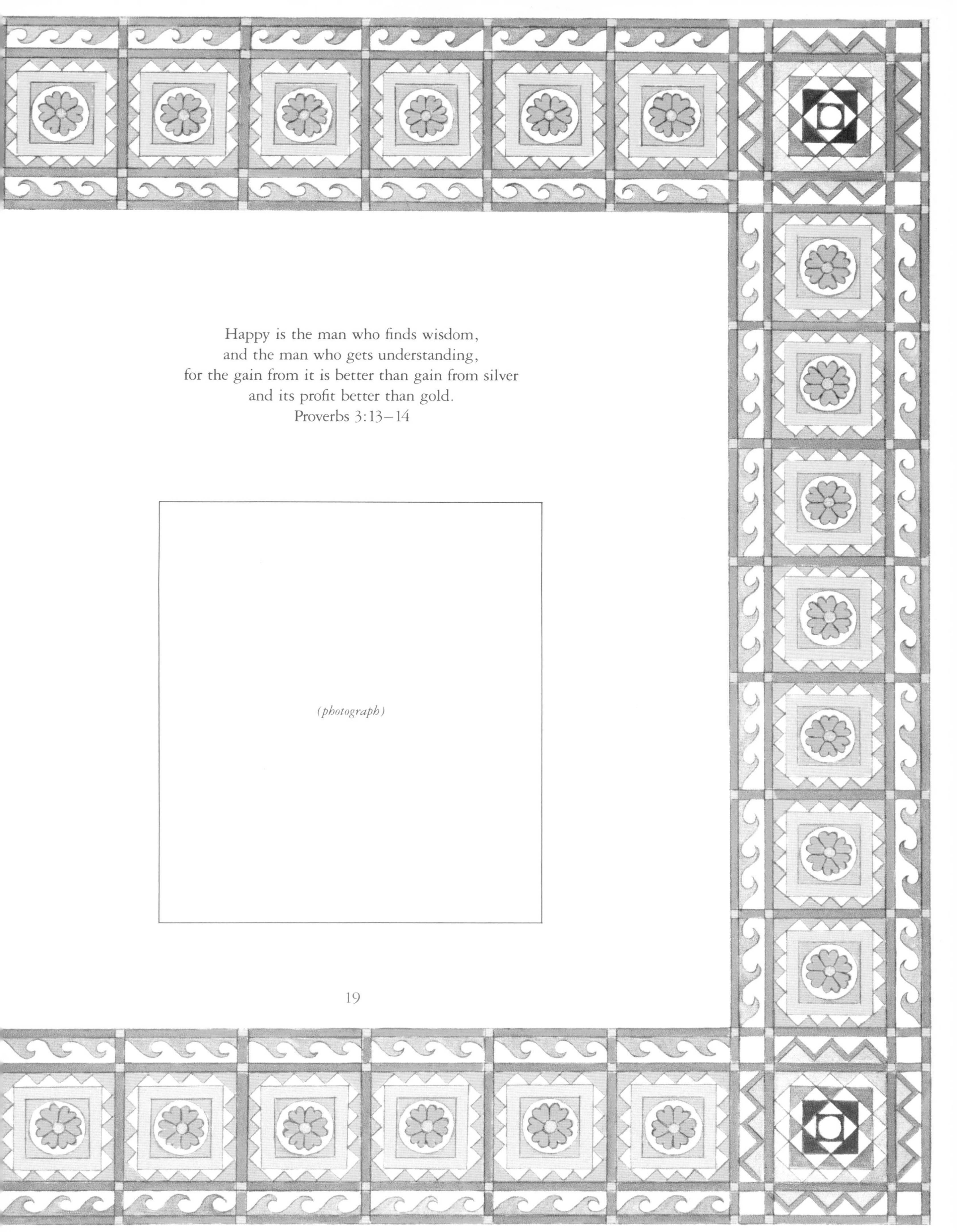

Happy is the man who finds wisdom,
and the man who gets understanding,
for the gain from it is better than gain from silver
and its profit better than gold.
Proverbs 3:13–14

(photograph)

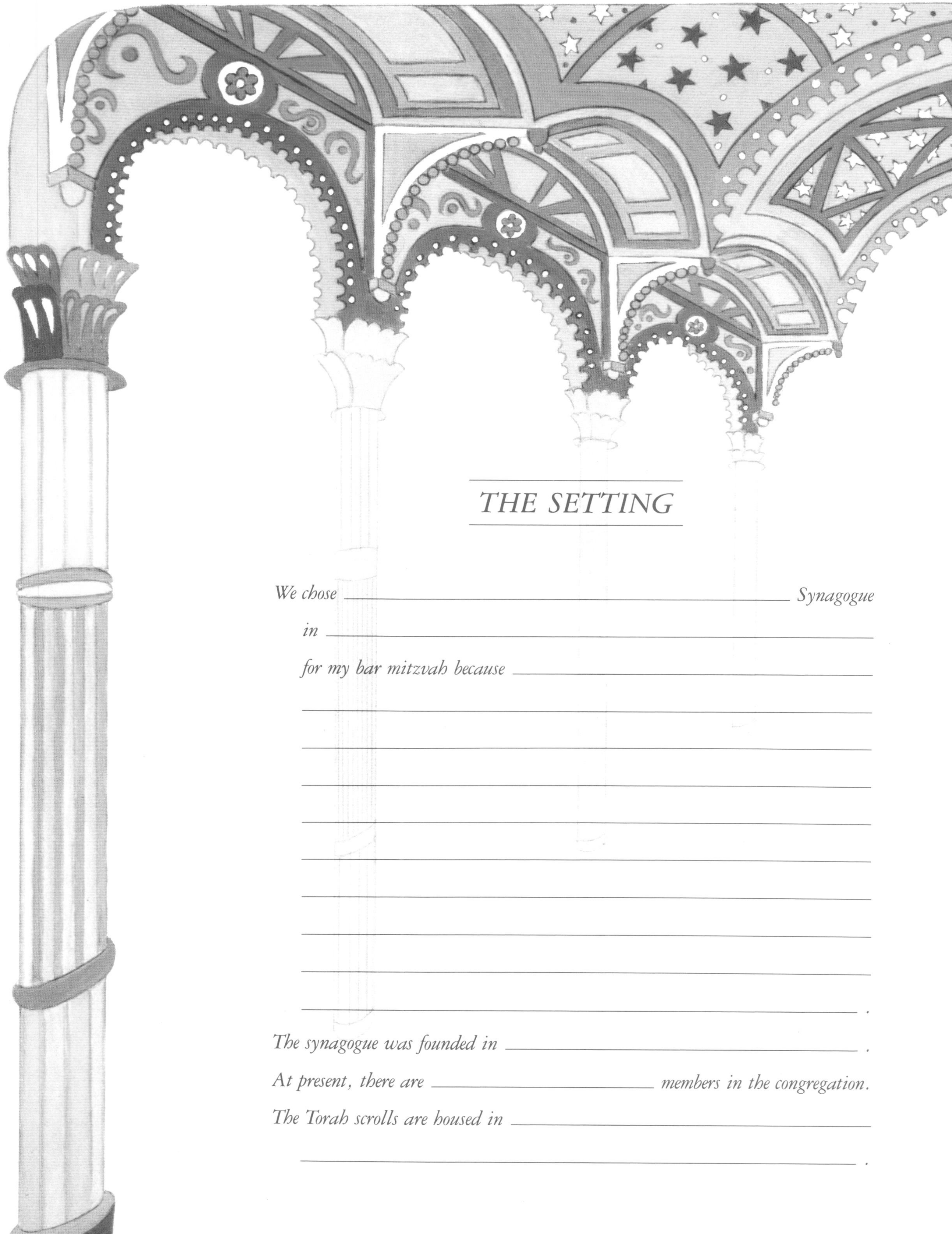

THE SETTING

We chose ______________________________ *Synagogue*

in ______________________________

for my bar mitzvah because ______________________________

____

____

____

____

____

____

____

____

______________________________ .

The synagogue was founded in ______________________________ .

At present, there are ______________ *members in the congregation.*

The Torah scrolls are housed in ______________________________

______________________________ .

AND ITS SIGNIFICANCE

Other friends and family members who have become bar or bat mitzvah here include ______________________________

The synagogue is special to my family and me because ______________________________

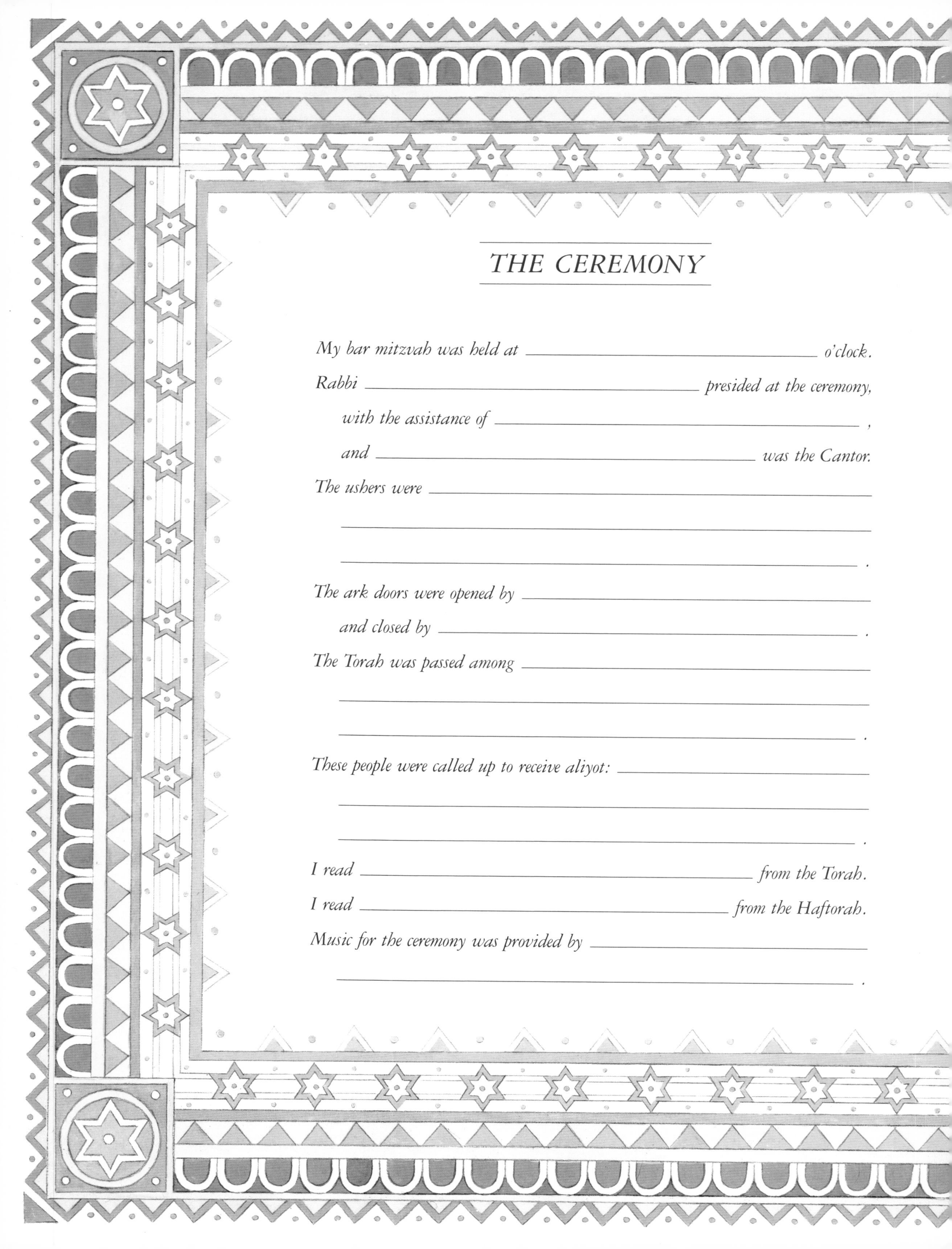

THE CEREMONY

My bar mitzvah was held at ______________________ *o'clock.*

Rabbi ______________________ *presided at the ceremony,*

with the assistance of ______________________ ,

and ______________________ *was the Cantor.*

The ushers were ______________________

____

______________________ .

The ark doors were opened by ______________________

and closed by ______________________ .

The Torah was passed among ______________________

____

______________________ .

These people were called up to receive aliyot: ______________________

____

______________________ .

I read ______________________ *from the Torah.*

I read ______________________ *from the Haftorah.*

Music for the ceremony was provided by ______________________

______________________ .

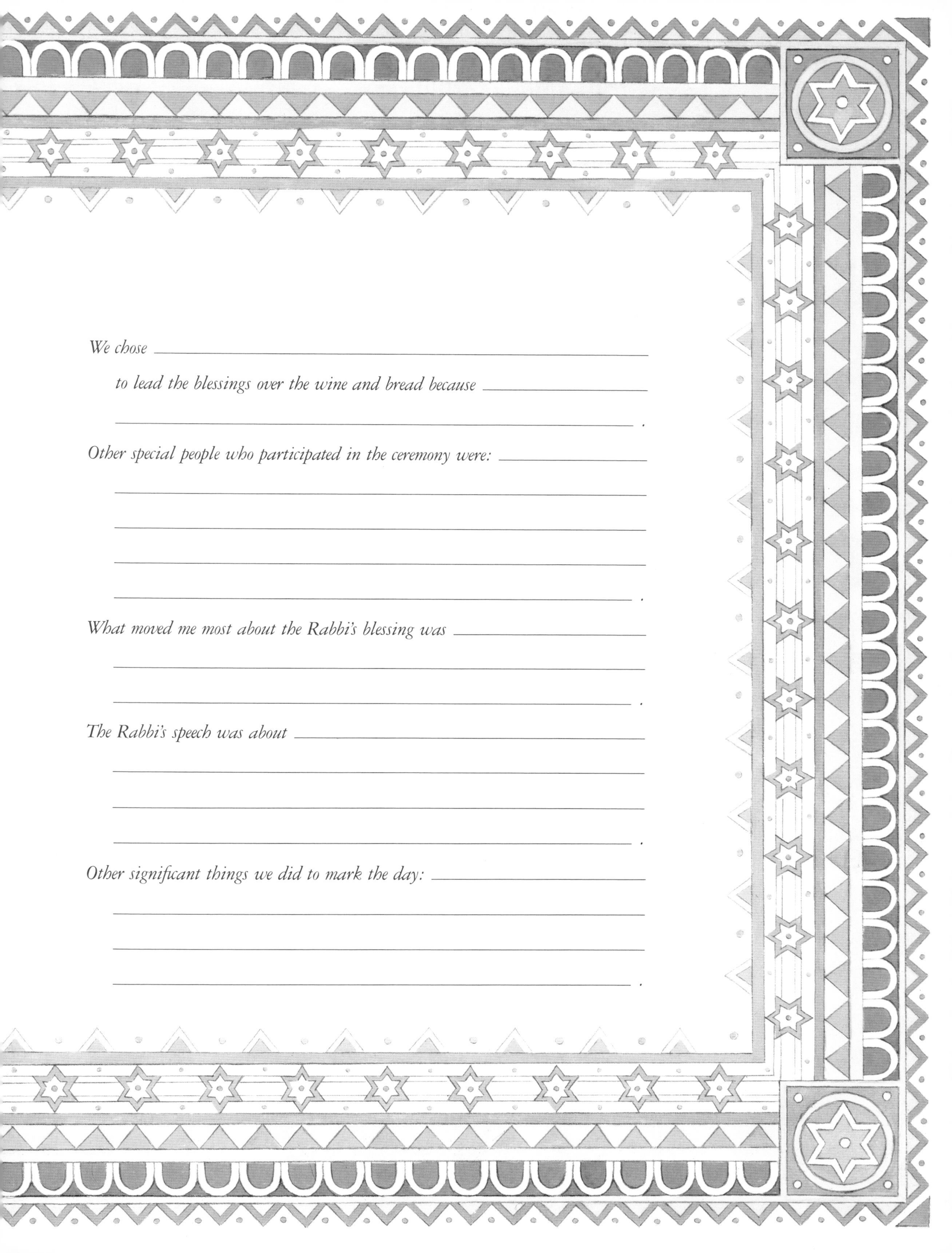

We chose ______________________________

to lead the blessings over the wine and bread because ______________

______________________________ .

Other special people who participated in the ceremony were: ______________

____

____

____

______________________________ .

What moved me most about the Rabbi's blessing was ______________

____

______________________________ .

The Rabbi's speech was about ______________________________

____

____

______________________________ .

Other significant things we did to mark the day: ______________

____

____

______________________________ .

THE TORAH

The following passages were read from the Torah: ___

Passages from the Torah

PRAYERS AND BLESSINGS

PRAYERS AND BLESSINGS

PRAYERS AND BLESSINGS

PRAYERS AND BLESSINGS

THE HAFTORAH

This is the Haftorah that I read at my bar mitzvah: ____________________

THE DERASHAH

This is the speech I gave at my bar mitzvah:

I chose to talk about these things because

PRAYERS FROM MY MOTHER ON THE DAY OF MY BAR MITZVAH

PRAYERS FROM MY FATHER ON THE DAY OF MY BAR MITZVAH

PRAYERS FROM MY GRANDPARENTS ON THE DAY OF MY BAR MITZVAH

PRAYERS FROM MY GRANDPARENTS ON THE DAY OF MY BAR MITZVAH

SPECIAL MOMENTS

The moment I most remember from my bar mitzvah ceremony was ______________

I felt most proud when ______________

Other special moments:

A MESSAGE FROM MY MOTHER

A MESSAGE FROM MY FATHER

MESSAGES AND WISHES FROM OTHERS

I received special wishes for my bar mitzvah from: ______________________

____

____

____

____

____

____

____

____

____.

Friends and relatives who could not attend but were with me in spirit: ________

____

____

____

____

____

____

____.

Here are some thoughts and wishes from my family, friends, and classmates:

THE GUESTS

THE GUESTS

THE GUESTS

THE GUESTS

GIFTS AND THANK YOU'S

I received the following gifts from:	*We sent thank-you's on:*

GIFTS AND THANK YOU'S

I received the following gifts from:

We sent thank-you's on:

GIFTS AND THANK YOU'S

I received the following gifts from: *We sent thank-you's on:*

GIFTS AND THANK YOU'S

I received the following gifts from: *We sent thank-you's on:*

THE CELEBRATION

The party was held at ______________________________

on ______________________________ ,

and it started at ______________________________ *o'clock.*

We chose the location because ______________________________

____

______________________________ .

Sitting at the dais were ______________________________

____

______________________________ .

Sitting with my mother and father were ______________________________

____

______________________________ .

My favorite part of the meal was ______________________________ ,

and everybody seemed to like ______________________________ .

The room and the tables were decorated with ______________________________

____

______________________________ .

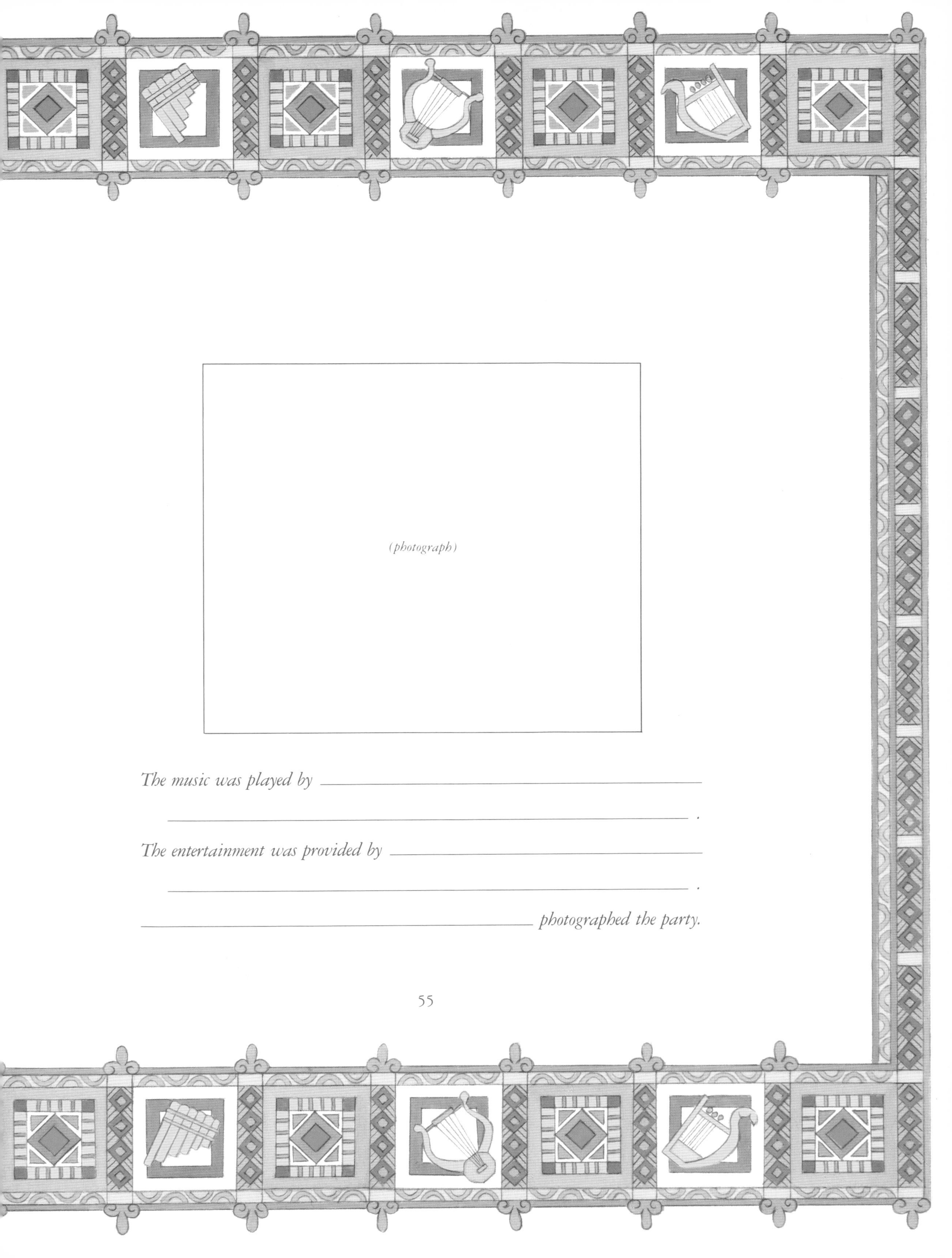

(photograph)

The music was played by ______________________________

______________________________ .

The entertainment was provided by ______________________________

______________________________ .

______________________________ *photographed the party.*

MEMORIES OF THE CELEBRATION

For me, the best part of the party was ____________________

____

____

____

____________________.

I had the most fun when ____________________

____

____

____________________.

The oldest member of my family at the party was ____________________

____________________,

and the youngest was ____________________.

____________________.

The funniest moment was ____________________

____

____

____________________.

The biggest surprise was ______________________________

____

____

____

____

____

______________________________ .

Although everyone had a good time, ______________________________

______________________________ *seemed to have the best time of all.*

It was especially good to see ______________________________

______________________________ .

The best part of the entertainment was ______________________________

____

____

____

______________________________ .

The celebration lasted until ______________________________ *o'clock.*

PHOTOGRAPHS AND MEMENTOS

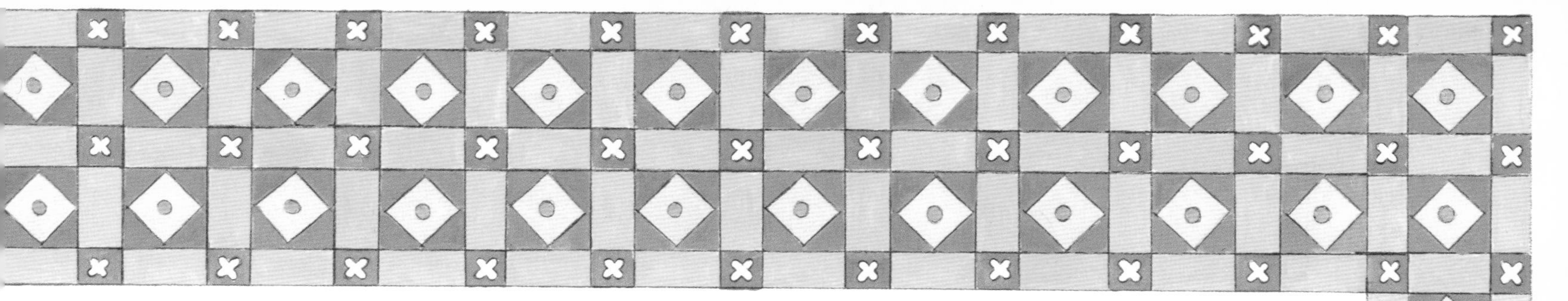

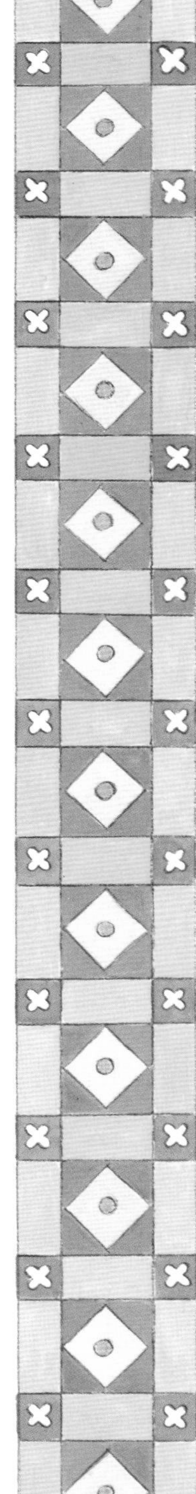

PHOTOGRAPHS AND MEMENTOS

PHOTOGRAPHS AND MEMENTOS

PHOTOGRAPHS AND MEMENTOS

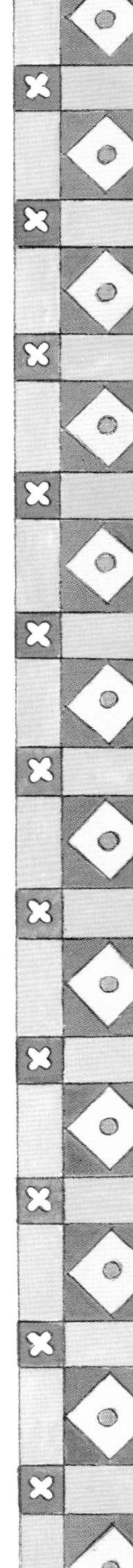

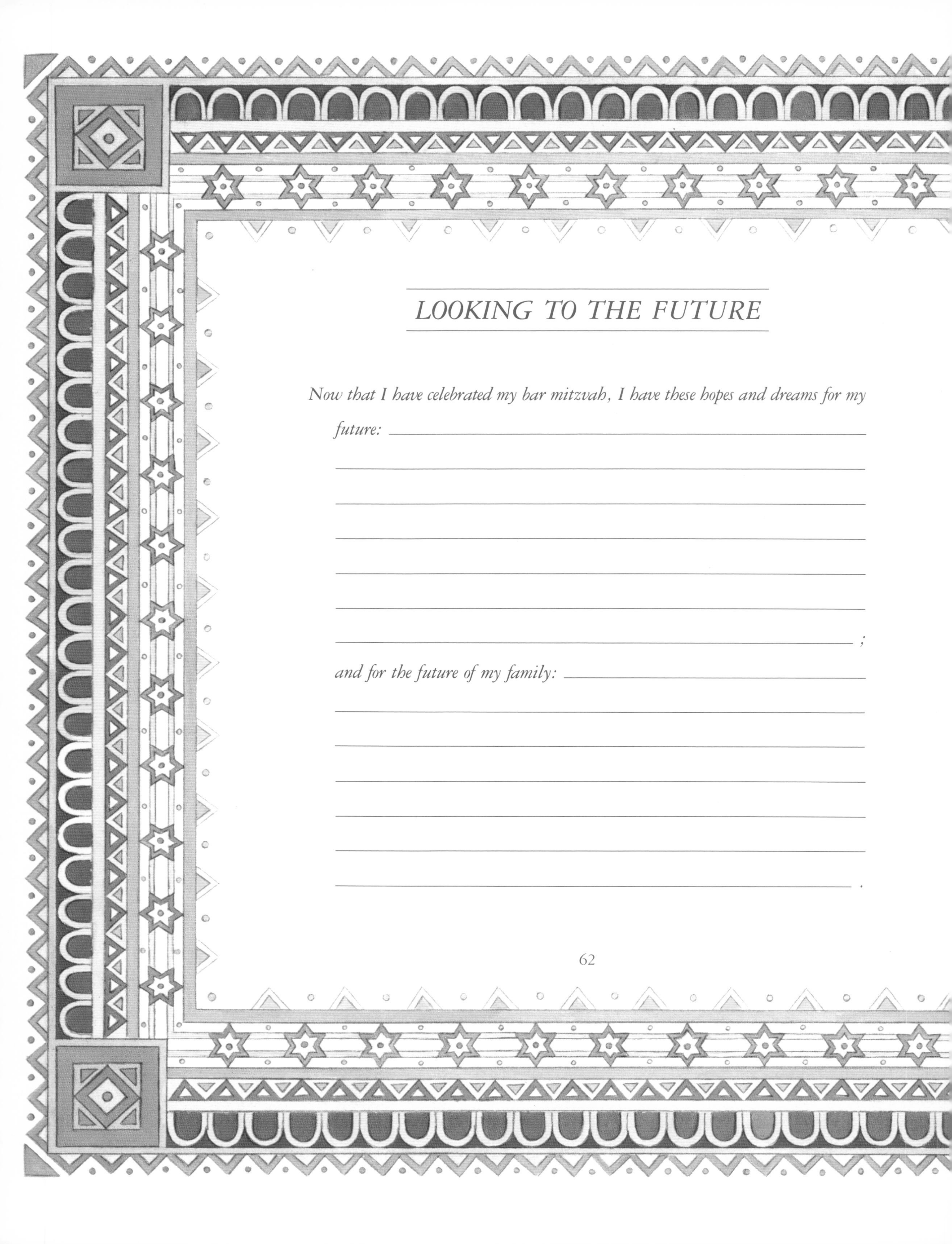

LOOKING TO THE FUTURE

Now that I have celebrated my bar mitzvah, I have these hopes and dreams for my future: ______________________________

____

____

____

____

____

______________________________ ;

and for the future of my family: ______________________________

____

____

____

____

____

______________________________ .

I hope to live in a world where ______________________________

____

____

____

____

____

____

______________________________ .

As a Jewish man, I feel the most important issue facing me today is __________

____

____

____

____

____

______________________________ .

ABOUT THE ART

The art that illuminates the pages of this book was inspired by Jewish art and artifacts, both ancient and modern, from many different countries. The artistic diversity displayed in these objects is a testimonial to the rich and varied legacy of Judaism. The sources of the border motifs are explained below.

6 and 7, 54–57: Florence Synagogue, via Farini, 1882.

8 and 9: Title page of a Hebrew book produced in Italy, 1730.

10 and 11, 32 and 33: German silver spice box, early 1700s.

12 and 13: Sabbath wine cup, Moscow, 1776.

14 and 15: Interior of the Synagogue at Strasbourg, France.

16–19: Mosaic pavement in the baths at Masada, Israel.

20 and 21: Interior of the Berlin Oranienburgerstrasse Synagogue, 1859–1866.

22–27, 62 and 63: Silver mezuzah case, Jerusalem, 1920s.

28–31: Interior of the Synagogue Samuel Halevi Abulafia, Toledo, Spain, 1360.

34 and 35: Isaac W. Wise Temple, Cincinnati, Ohio.

36–39: Detail of gold embroidery on the border of the ark curtain in the Old Synagogue, Prague, 1625–1660.

40 and 41: Polish silver Torah pointer, mid 1700s.

42 and 43: Wall painting in Kamionka Strumilowa Synagogue, Poland, 1730.

44 and 45: Illuminated manuscript page, Yemen, San'a, 1475.

46–49: End piece from a German Hebrew publication, 1785.

50–53: Polish silver Sabbath candlesticks, 1887.

58–61: Isaac W. Wise Temple, Cincinnati, Ohio.